Best wishes

David and Michael
from Dianne & Wendy.

ABORIGINAL MYTHS

ABORIGINAL MYTHS

by

SRETEN BOZIC

in conjunction with

ALAN MARSHALL

GOLD STAR PUBLICATIONS
MELBOURNE

First published by
Gold Star Publications, 1972

National Library of Australia card number and I.S.B.N. 07260 0113 9

Published in Australia by
Gold Star Publications (Aust) Pty Ltd.,
Hawthorn, Victoria, Australia, 3123.

Printed by Wilke and Company Limited.
37 Browns Road, Clayton, Victoria.

Contents

Illustrations

Introduction

A tall dignified Aboriginal, resembling a warrior from the vastness of Northern Australia came out from the bush and walked with apparent intensity down to the Mandorah Resort. Instead of a spear he carried a Didgeridoo. His body and muscles seemed to be moving in rhythm to the ageless roar of the Didgeridoo and the sound of the Clapping Sticks. He is known by the name of Mulluk and the Europeans have, for some reason, prefixed it with 'Jim'.

For many years Mulluk has entertained the tourists at Mandorah and Mika Beach by performing the Corroboree, the ancient Aboriginal ceremony. The Europeans applaud him and snap him with their cameras but Mulluk hardly notices. He performs the native dance not for the sake of demonstrating it for the whites but because the dance and the music are an integral part of his life and by doing this he is keeping the cultural heritage of his race alive.

Both these resorts, Mandorah and Mika Beach, are across the Bay from Darwin, located close to West Point. The only road to this area is a bush track encircling Darwin Bay, stretching through mangrove country for a hundred miles. In the centre of the Peninsula lies Delissaville, an Aboriginal settlement. In the beginning of this century there were several Aboriginal tribes living in this part of the Australian North who had managed to preserve their ancient way of life in a traditional bush environment. Inevitably, contact with civilization brought about a destructive effect, totally wiping out the social structure of tribal society, and, with this gone, the great cultural heritage began to decline and, with it, went Art, the Dance, Mythology and Oral Literature.

Coming into contact with the Aboriginals, the Europeans soon brought alcohol and disease and from then on these things proved to be sure killers. The intrusion of European civilization into the lives of the Aboriginals did not only mean a rapid deterioration in their culture but caused whole tribes to totally vanish and others to be decimated. The remaining members of the Laragia, Warei, Nangiomeri, Wogadj and other tribes from

this part of Northern Australia are grouped within the Delissaville settlement. Among them lives 'Jim' Mulluk with a handful of his men from the Ngulugwongga tribe. This tribe was commonly called 'Mulluk Mulluk'. It is the name of 'Jim's' Clan and because the Mulluk Mulluks were the last Chiefs of the Ngulugwongga tribe the tribe became known by the name of its head man.

Most of the tourists who come to the Top End are ferried from Darwin to Mandorah and Mika Beach. Almost every day Mulluk with a group of native men walks from the bush down to the resort to perform the Corroboree for the cameras. Nature has not imbued Mulluk with a warrior spirit but rather with the tender love of a poet. During the nights he sits by the camp fire somewhere on the sandy beaches or deep in the bush and plays the Didgeridoo while his native contemporaries dance. He creates the dances and accompanies them with the appropriate traditional tunes about his ancestral heroes from the Dreamtime, the indeterminate past of the Aboriginals, and by performing these songs and dances he communicates with the ancient characters of his race. With the sincerity of a poet he deeply believes that those ancestral heroes lived in this country during the long past, and were forced by nature or sometimes by their own will to change into animals or were metamorphosed into rocks and plants thereby creating the present wildlife and scenery as it is now known.

Usually in the afternoon Mulluk appears with his dancing team in the clearing behind the Mandorah resort. The natives perform several dances like 'Hunting the Buffalo', 'Crab Dance', and so on. During the Corroboree Mulluk does not play the Didgeridoo as usual but sings and beats time with wooden sticks and conducts the entire ceremony with that sound only. Next to him is a Didgeridoo player accompanying his voice and movement with the roaring sound of the pipe and by amalgamating all of these and by the gestures of his arms and hands he invokes an emotional excitement among the Aboriginal dancers inspiring them and directing their course of action and movement. All of this creates a traditional illustration of a remote culture in the life of Stone Age Man.

There are some afternoons when Mulluck does not appear from

the bush. The owners of Mandorah resort are alarmed and search for him through the bush and on the beaches in an attempt to persuade him to come and dance in front of hundreds of tourists; but there is no power in the world which can make him change his ways. He is not tired of dancing, but from time to time he directs his attention to other Aboriginal activities, a visit to the totemic or sacred sites in the bush, fishing or hunting with his spear and at these times the display at the resort is for him, of secondary importance.

I befriended Mulluk several years ago and often stayed with him and other natives. He and his men took me hunting, we stayed in the bush for days living in the traditional way of the natives; on other occasions we went through the coastal areas searching for turtles and crabs; we visited the swamps in the low country close to the beaches and gathered the yams and edible roots—wherever we went we moved through Aboriginal country bearing strong reminders of their culture and way of life. Passing by totemic sites, natural phenomena and various species of flora and fauna, Mulluk and his men would tell me the stories from the Dreamtime explaining in a simplified way how that particular object or species had come into existence. In the evening sitting by the campfire in the wilderness of the bush, or on the remote beaches, the Aboriginals told me endless stories about the ancient events or ancestral heroes from their mythological past.

Some of those stories recorded from Mulluk and his men I gave to Alan Marshall and we collaborated in putting those myths and legends into a form adequate for European readers. Care was taken to preserve the native way of expression and the original flavour of the stories; I hope we succeeded.

SRETEN BOZIC
1972.

MANARK, the MOTHER KANGAROO
and MEMEMBEL, the PORPOISE

In the Dreamtime when animals were the people, the Porpoise was a woman called Memembel. She liked the sea and went often to the beach. Sometimes she stayed there for many days. She made her own camp fire on the sand and lived lonely by the seaside. When other people came to the shore to fish they saw her and they said, 'Memembel, come with us to the bush. We are going to sing and dance. Next day we'll go to hunt. Come with us, Memembel.'

'No,' she answered. 'I like to stay here. One day I'll have many children. I want to show them how to swim. I'll show it to them so well that they will all swim as far as the sea goes. After, when they grow up they will know the water as well as you know the bush.'

Memembel never went to join the other people. She kept herself on the beach and no one came any more to call her, or even to talk to her. She was left alone and stayed unmarried. But as time passed by she bore many children. She had so many of them that they became lazy and ugly. She was always hoping that the next she would have would be the better one. She wanted her children to be beautiful and cheerful but none of them turned out to be that way.

'Since all my children are lazy and ugly then I will go and get to me the most beautiful child in the country,' she said to herself one day. Memembel went straight into the bush after that. Not very far from the beach she saw two tracks. They were footprints in the sand and one of them was small and the other was big. 'Look,' she said. 'Manark, the Mother Kangaroo, and her child,

Chormong, passed here. I'll follow them. Manark has the best looking child in the country.

She walked all day following the tracks but she did not see anyone. About sunset she came to a waterhole and there they were. Manark was tired of the long journey and after she had drunk water she went to sleep in the shade. But little Chormong, he was playing around. Memembel went close to him. She did not want to grab the child because the boy would yell and it would wake his mother. Memembel began to dance. She never was a good dancer but she was the funny one. Little Chormong watched her and started to giggle.

As she danced, Memembel began to move backwards and she kept going deeper and deeper into the bush. Little Chormong followed her and his giggle grew into a laugh. Memembel kept going backwards then suddenly dashed behind some trees. Little Chormong could not see her any more. He thought she had run away and he hurried forward to see where she had gone. As soon as he was passing the trees Memembel grabbed him in her arms and ran towards the beach.

When Manark woke up she could not see her child. She went and looked around, and then she smelled the track.

'Someone was here and took away my child,' she said.

The track was still fresh and she smelled it strongly. She ran after Memembel quickly but Memembel was far ahead and she could not reach her. But when she reached the beach she saw Memembel and Memembel was taking Chormong down to the sea.

'Give my child back!' called Manark and she rushed towards Memembel.

'I want to keep him,' said Memembel. 'He is mine now. You go back and have another boy for yourself.'

'He is mine!' yelled Manark. She was so angry that she rushed at Memembel and hit her hard on the top of her head. The head

19

broke off and a big hole was left there. When Memembel saw this she was so angry she grabbed a stick and hit Manark on her arms. She did it so hard that both Manark's arms were broken.
After this Manark went back with her boy to the bush.
'From now on I'm going to be a Kangaroo,' she said. 'I'll have a big pouch to keep my child in and then my child will never be taken away from me again.'
So she became a kangaroo. But she still keeps her broken arms and that is why the kangaroo's front legs are so short. They are broken arms.
But Memembel had a big hole on her head and now she was so ugly. She said to herself, 'I'm going to go away from everyone. I will be a porpoise and I am going to live in the sea from now on.'
The porpoise still has a broken head. When he swims in the sea a big jet of water comes out into the air from the hole in his head.

KARRA-KARRA, the CUCKOO and CUT-CUT, SPIRIT MAN

One stormy night Karra-Karra the Cuckoo Woman travelled with her husband along the beach. They had with them many young children and they were looking for a place to hide from the rain.

'We have to find a rock shelter or a cave,' said her husband. He was walking ahead carrying the spears and the fire-stick.

'How far have we to go?' asked Karra-Karra. She carried some of the youngest children and led those who could walk. She felt tired of the long journey and was left behind by her husband.

'If we don't see any shelter in the dark we will find it in the morning,' she told her children.

The children felt cold and wet and were crying. Their noise awoke Cut-Cut and he said to himself, 'Look, there are so many children. I never saw a mother who bore so many of them.'

Cut-Cut went up into the air and rolled many waves of the dark over the country. The waves were like the clouds—they made the night longer and kept it dark for many days.

Karra-Karra's husband was walking along the beach as though nothing had happened. His wife was left behind in the dark and they could not talk any longer because of the distance. Karra-Karra was worried about the children and from time to time she called each one of them by name to make sure they are all with her and not lost in the dark.

When at last the night was over Karra-Karra looked around. She could not see her husband. There was not even his track on the sand.

'My husband is lost,' she said. 'The night has been so long and dark. He has walked some other way.'

Now Cut-Cut came on the beach and told her, 'Your husband is far away, he will never find you.'

'He is around,' said Karra-Karra. 'He will come.'

'Look at this country; those rocks and hills—you have never been here before.'

'No,' said Karra-Karra.

'Your husband does not know this country. How will he find you?'

'What am I going to do?' asked Karra-Karra.

'I can find your husband,' said Cut-Cut.

'All right, you go and bring him.'

'No,' said Cut-Cut, 'first you have to give me one of your children, then I'll go.'

'Go away,' said Karra-Karra. 'I don't want to let you have my children. Go away!'

Cut-Cut went away. A few days later he came back. Karra-Karra was still on the beach waiting for her husband. She had made a fire on the sand near the sea but she did not have a spear to hunt with and she had no food.

'It is hard with so many children without father,' said Cut-Cut.

'All right, go and bring my husband,' said Karra-Karra.

Cut-Cut took one of the children and went away. A few days passed and then he came back.

'I looked around,' he said, 'but I could not find him. I have to look further and you have to give me one more child.'

Cut-Cut kept coming back like this until he took the last child. The child was still a baby and was asleep on its mother's breast. Karra-Karra gave him away and said, 'Hold him gently; if he wakes he will cry.'

She stayed on the beach and waited for a day. When the night came she did not make a fire. 'My husband will never come back,' she said to herself. 'I am alone now. Cut-Cut will come again and he will take me away.'

She ran from the beach to the bush. As soon as she was amongst the trees she changed herself into a Cuckoo. From then on she never made her nest because she knew if she tried to raise little ones Cut-Cut would come again and take them away.

MICHERIN, the DINGO

A long time ago when animals were people the Dingo was a black fellow. His name was Micherin. He was always hungry and wandered through the bush looking for food but he was a bad hunter who spent many days without catching anything.

'I will die if I don't eat,' he said to himself. 'I will have to get something.'

In his country there grew many chilli bushes. He had never tasted the chillies before but now he thought it would be better to eat the chillies than to starve. He picked many chillies and began to eat them but the chillies were hot and his mouth and tongue began to burn. Micherin became frightened. He thought he had eaten something which would kill him and he called out 'Help me! I'll die! Help me!'

The Black Hawk man, Wak, heard him and he called from the air, 'What have you eaten, my friend?'

'I ate the fire. It is still in my mouth.'

'You have eaten bush chilli,' Wak, the Black Hawk man said to him. 'You should not eat them.'

'There is nothing else to eat round here,' said Micherin. 'I had to eat the chilli.'

'Go to the beach,' Wak ordered. 'There is an old dead turtle there. I have just eaten half of it but half is left.'

Micherin went down to the sea and found the turtle but the meat was too hard and he could not eat it.

'I have to put the turtle on the fire and the meat will be good,' he said to himself. He took his fire-sticks and began to rub them together to make a fire. It was just after the rain and the wood

29

was wet so he could not make a fire with the fire-sticks but he kept rubbing them harder and harder and as he did so ten big blisters on his hands grew so big that at last he said to himself, 'Look, I don't have my fingers any more. They have become blisters now. I will be a dingo from now on.'

He was not even able to speak any longer. The only sound he could make was 'Owww, oww, oww! That is the way he yells out because the hot chilli has burnt his mouth and tongue. And that is why the dingo has to eat raw meat for the rest of his life.

MUNGI, the TURTLE
and THE BATIGON BROTHERS

Turtle Man, Mungi, was good singer. He never stayed to live at one place and travelled through the country carrying with him only knocking sticks. He did not care much about hunting or looking for a wife and having children. He only loved his singing and he wanted other people to enjoy it.

'Come to our place and sing for us,' the two Batigon Brothers told him.

'Where is your place?' asked Mungi.

'Down by the sea, on a big rock. It is our home. It is nice there. You would like it.'

'I cannot go,' said Mungi. 'I have never before been to the big water and I don't know how to swim.'

'Don't you worry; we'll take care of you,' they told him.

The Batigon Brothers carried Mungi over the water to the big rock. The rock was off the beach in the sea. Never before had Mungi been surrounded by water and he did not like this place. But he did not want to let the Batigon Brothers down and he stayed on the rock for several days singing and knocking his sticks. Then he said, 'I should go back now. It has been a long time since I left my country.'

'Why should you go?' they said to him. 'We give tucker to you here. You can stay forever.'

'I have to go. I like to travel. When I am travelling my singing is going with me to all the places over the whole country.'

The Brothers did not like him to leave them and they said, 'Stay longer here. We'll show you how to swim. When you know how to swim, you can go across the water to your country by

yourself and then you will come back to see us again.'

'Come on, show me how to swim,' begged Mungi.

'We'll show you tomorrow,' they told him.

But the next day came and other days came and passed by. Mungi sang all the time but the Batigon Brothers never showed him how to swim. At last Mungi saw that he would have to make his own way back to the land by himself. One day when the brothers were busy fishing, Mungi began to walk from the rock to the beach. As he went on he stepped deeper and deeper into the sea. The level of the water reached his mouth and he was about to be drowned.

The two Batigon Brothers saw him going away and they rushed to stop him. One of them came from the front of Mungi and the other came from behind him. They lifted him up into the air from the water and brought him back to the rock.

'I'll sing for you all the time,' Mungi told them. 'You saved my life.'

He began to sing and he knocked the sticks against each other so hard that both the pieces of wood broke.

'Look, I can't sing any more,' he said. 'I need the wood to make new singing sticks.'

'I'll go to land and bring them to you,' said one of the brothers. 'What kind of wood do you need?'

'I need a big hollow log. That is the only wood I can cut my singing sticks from.'

'No one makes singing sticks from a big log,' they said.

'No one sings as good as I do.'

The Batigon Brothers brought him a big hollow log. They hurried him to cut it straight away and make the sticks so that they could hear him singing again. But Mungi went first and carved crosslines all over the log, then he said:

'That's all. It is evening now. I will cut the sticks from the log tomorrow.'

During the night when the Batigon Brothers were asleep Mungi went into the log. He jumped with it into the sea and began to swim to the beach. The Batigon Brothers saw him. They did not want him to go away and they threw their spears at him. Mungi pulled in his legs, arms and head into the hollow of the log and the spears hit the wood but they could do no harm to him. He swam to the beach. The Brothers threw many spears after him but he protected himself in the hollow of the log. He was a man no longer but was a turtle that swam in the sea.

CHILBRUK, the BLACK AND WHITE DUCK and WOREMBEN, the CROCODILE

In the Dreamtime Chilbruk the Black and White Duck used to be the wife of Woremben, the Crocodile. They lived in the bush between a big swamp and the sea.

There was not much bush food around. But even if there was plenty, Woremben never went out to look for it. He was an old man and he slept all day in the shade. It was the job for his young wife Chilbruk. She had to spend every day in the bush searching for tucker.

One day she did not feel like going out any more.

'I'll stay here and lie in the shade, as you do,' she told her husband. 'When we get hungry we'll both go to look for food.'

'You have to go,' he said. 'I'm an old man and you are young. That is why I married you, to look after me.'

'I do not want to look after you,' said Chilbruk. 'You go and look for food.'

'I'll make you go,' Woremben said holding his fighting stick.

Chilbruk went into the bush and stayed there all day. In the bush she dug many perri, the roots of the yams. She ate as much as she could but she could not finish them all. What was left of the perri she carried away with her. When she came back to the camp she buried the perri in the ground and then she went to her husband.

'Chilbruk, did you bring any food?' asked Woremben.

'I could not find any yams,' she told him.

'We have to sleep hungry now,' said Woremben, 'but tomorrow you get up early and don't you come back without food.'

The next day Chilbruk went to the bush again. She wandered

41

around all day but this time she did not find any yams. She came home hungry. Her husband was angry for a while and then he went to sleep. But Chilbruk stayed up by the camp fire. She waited until Woremben was asleep and then she walked into the dark. Not far away from the fire, behind the bush, there was the perri which she had buried. She dug them out now and began to eat them.

'What are you eating?' called her husband.

'Nothing,' she said.

'I hear you eating.'

'I am trying to eat the bark of the tree. It does not taste nice.'

'It is the yams you are eating,' yelled Woremben. 'You are lying to me.'

He rushed at his wife and hit her with a stick. Chilbruk turned on him and scratched him with her nails all over his body. His skin was cut into pieces. Woremben screamed with pain and hit his wife several times on the head with a stick. Chilbruk fell down and died. But as soon as she touched the ground she changed herself into the Black and White Duck and flew away towards the swamp. On her head there were two white lines. These are the marks where Woremben hit her.

With the skin cut all over his body, Woremben was ashamed to go anywhere. 'Look,' he said to himself. 'I am ugly now. When others see me they will laugh. I would like to become a crocodile,' and he became a crocodile and went to the water to live there. But since he was once a human being he can come out of the water and go into the bush whenever he wants to. His skin is still scratched all over. These are the marks of Chilbruk's nails.

MAGGI, the BARRAMUNDI FISH

In the Dreamtime the Barramundi Fish was a man named Maggi. He was young and was about to marry and the girl he was going to marry was called Inmura.

Inmura was promised to him while both of them were still children. Since that time Maggi had never let this girl go out of his sight. He was so much in love with her that he would not go to the bush to hunt. He always kept close to Inmura thinking somebody would steal her.

'You can't marry,' Inmura's father told him once. 'You will never be a man.'

'I'm grown up,' said Maggi.

'Yes, but you don't know how to hunt. You can't fight and you can't even throw a spear.'

'You wait,' said Maggi, 'I'll show you one day.'

He left the camp and went into the bush. He decided to stay away from the others and hunt his own food and throw the spear day and night. He made up his mind not to come back until he was sure he would be the best fighter and spear man in all the country.

It took him a long time to learn all this. When he came back to his tribe the years had passed by. During that time many children were born and many old people died. Inmura's father had died and Inmura was now about to be given to an old man for his wife.

'She is my girl,' yelled Maggi. 'She can't marry anyone else.'

'She has to marry the old man,' they told him. 'He needs a young wife to look after him.'

Maggi decided to fight for his girl. He knew how to throw the

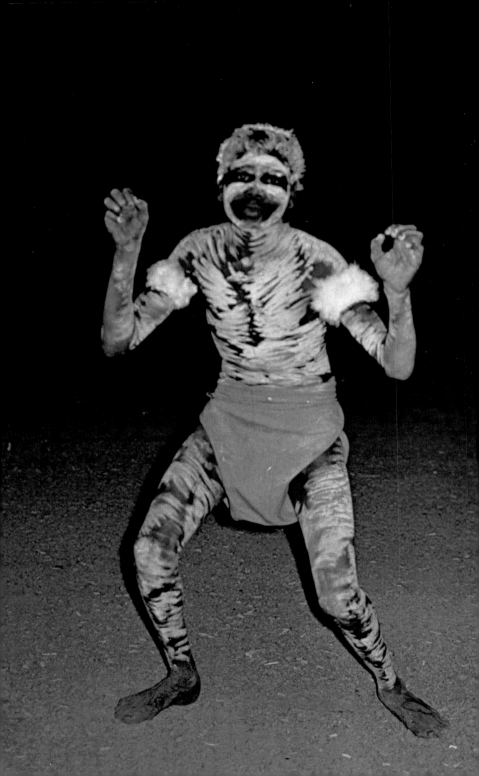

spear well and he would be able to face the best fighter. But there were many men in the tribe and he could not fight against all of them.

It was much better to wait for a while. That evening they were holding a corroboree. As soon as night fell the men left the camp and went to the bush to sing and dance. The only people left in the camp were the children and the women.

'I am taking my girl away now,' said Maggi.

He grabbed Inmura and ran with her to the bush. There was no-one to follow him at that time but Maggi knew that as soon as the corroboree was finished the men from the tribe would be back and they would be after him.

'The men will follow our track,' Maggi told Inmura. 'We have to run as far as the country goes.'

They ran a long way and they stopped on the seashore. Now they could go no further. It was night. They made love but they did not go to sleep. Maggi knew that the men were after him and he said to Inmura, 'I have to make lots of spears.'

'I will help you make them,' said Inmura.

At day break the men from the tribe appeared on the rocks overlooking the shore. But by now Maggi had a big heap of spears. He threw some of the spears towards them. It was a long way but the spears flew through the air straight and fast. When the men from the tribe saw them coming they rushed behind the rocks for shelter.

Later they appeared again. Maggi had to force them back by throwing more spears. It continued like this all that day. As soon as he threw the spears Inmura made new ones and this kept them fighting all the time. At evening Inmura became tired and she said to her husband, 'There is no wood left to make any more spears. We must run away now.'

'We can't run,' Maggi said. 'The sea is behind us.'

'When you are without spears they will come here and kill

49

you,' said Inmura. 'You stay here. Let me go back. If I go back to them they will leave you alone.'

'No,' he said. 'I don't want to live on the land any more. I am going to the sea and I will become a fish.'

He threw his last spear at the men of the tribe then he took Inmura and went to live in the water. Maggi changed himself into a Barramundi fish and Inmura went with him to be his wife forever. They don't want to live on the land ever again and that is why when fish come out of the water they die.

NAREK, the COCKATOO
and MAJEN, the BLACK DUCK

A long time ago Cockatoo-Woman, Narek, was married to Black-Duck Man, Majen. After their marriage, she went with her husband to live in his country. Majen lived on a big lake. There was lots of food for him there in the water and amongst the tall grass and the bushes which grew in the swamp and around the lake. He was very proud of this area and he would never go to live at any other place in the world. But Narek was not happy about it.

'It stinks here,' she once said to her husband. 'The water is everywhere and I don't know how to swim.'

'This is what my country looks like,' Majen told her.

'Before you married me,' said Narek, 'you said you have a beautiful place for us to live. This is not it, Majen. Let us go and live somewhere in the bush country. Here the water is everywhere and I don't know how to swim.'

'Wait and see, and I'll do something,' Majen told her. 'I'm going to splash out most of the water from the lake. When the water goes out the trees will grow here then there will be only swamp left and I will still be able to swim in it. Then it will be beautiful country for both of us.'

But Majen was never able to drain the lake. And what was worse the season of heavy rain began and many creeks ran down to the lake. The level of its water rose and it flooded all the surrounding country and rose up to the branches of the highest tree.

'You see what has happened now,' Narek told her husband.

'All right,' he said to her, 'if you want to go to some better place, you go, but me—I can't leave my country. I'm staying here and I'll swim in the water.'

'I'll stay with you, of course,' said Narek, 'but I can't swim. Majen, you'll have to make me a canoe. While you swim I'll sit in it and follow you all the time. Majen had to look for a canoe tree. On the other side of the lake was a big forest. It was the only place where he could find the canoe tree and Majen swam across the lake to get there.

Narek was left alone to wait for her husband to come back with the canoe. While he was away the rain changed into a big storm and the level of the water rose even higher.

'I can't swim,' said Narek to herself, 'I have to run away from here.'

But all the area was flooded and the night was coming. Narek could not run away. She went to hide in the hollow of a big tree. She felt safe there for a while, but later the water rose higher. It reached the entrance to the hollow and it still kept rising. Narek had to climb up through the hollow but at the top of the hollow there was no way to get out.

During the night, Majen came back with a canoe he had made. He looked everywhere around but he could not find Narek.

'She is drowned,' he said. 'I'll never see her again.'

He felt a big sorrow because of his wife and he changed himself into the Black Duck and stayed to live on the lake for ever.

Trapped in the hollow Narek said to herself, 'The storm has drowned my husband. He will never come back. I don't want to be woman any more.'

She changed herself into a Cockatoo and dug the tree with her bill to get out from the hollow.

55

NURRUN, the EMU
and MANOR, the PLAIN TURKEY

In the Dreamtime Emu-Man Nurrun and Plain Turkey Woman Manor were husband and wife but they did not stay together for long. Before the marriage Manor never knew about fire and Nurrun had a lot of trouble teaching his wife how to handle it.

On the night when they were married they made a big fire. They cooked their tucker on it and ate the food by the light of it. But the fire soon burnt low and Manor said, 'Should I put more wood on the fire?'

'No,' Nurrun told her, 'we have to be careful. The fire can burn us.'

It was a cold night. Nurrun dug a big hole in the sand by the fire and lay down in it to sleep.

'Dear,' he said to his wife, 'cover me with the sand. Like that I'll be warm all night.'

Manor began to pour the sand into the hole to cover her husband. But with the sand she poured also the hot ash from around the fire. The ash fell on Nurrun and burnt his wings.

'I burnt you!' cried Manor. 'I'm a bad wife.'

'All right, we'll forget it. But be careful with the fire from now on.'

A few days later Nurrun had to go into the bush to make a Madjgindi, the Corroboree for men. His wife did not feel like staying alone in the Camp and she said, 'I'm afraid to be just by myself in the dark. Can I come with you?'

'You can't dear. Madjgindi is only for men, not for women.'

'It is night,' said Manor. 'How can I stay alone. I'm afraid.'

'Make a big fire,' Nurrun told her. 'When the fire is big it drives

57

the dark away.'

Manor stayed and made a big fire. But it was a windy night and the tall grass in the bush was dry. The wind blew out the fire and lit the bush. It made a bush fire. The fire swung around the camp and the flames were everywhere.

Manor climbed up a tree and went to the top of it, but the bark of the tree began to burn and the fire came up to her.

'I'll die if I don't run,' she told herself. She could not jump down and she could not stay in the tree. All the bush was on fire and she had to run somewhere. 'I'll go into the air,' she said to herself.

She changed into a Plain Turkey and flew away.

The bush fire swung through the whole area. It also caught Nurrun at the time when he was making his Madjgindi.

'It is Manor,' he said to himself. 'She did it again.'

He could not fly away because his wings were still burnt from the night when his wife threw ash on him. He had to run through the bush. As he did it the fire caught him and burnt the rest of his wings and many of his feathers.

'I wish I had long and fast legs,' he said.

He changed himself into an Emu and he ran through the bush much faster than the fire was going. This is why the Emu runs when fire comes to his country and the Plain Turkey flies from the flames.

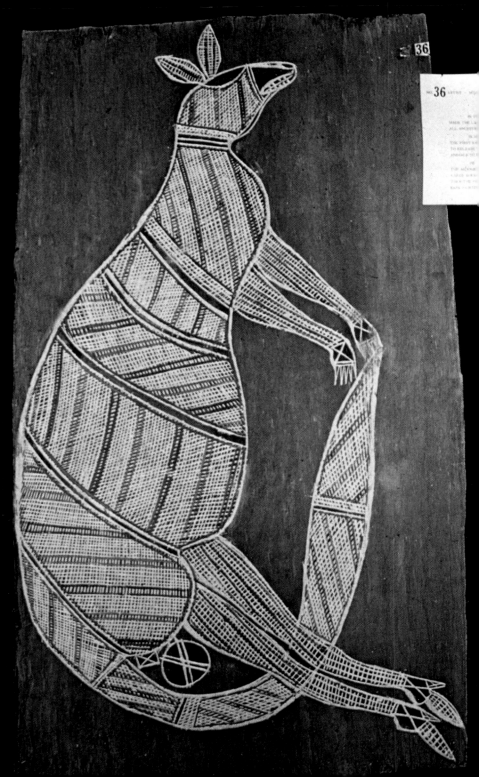

WILAR, the CROCODILE

One day in the Dreamtime two sisters, Indra, the older one and Jippi, the younger one were on a long journey through the country. When they became tired of walking they sat down to have a rest near a billabong. Wilar, the crocodile saw them and said to himself, 'I am going to have one of those girls for myself.'

He crept close to them and grabbed Indra. The young sister grew frightened and ran away screaming.

Wilar took Indra to a cave. He was hungry but he did not want to eat her. He left her and went back to the water. There he caught many fish to fill up his belly.

When he came back to the cave Indra was asleep. He did not want to touch her yet so first he put a lot of mud and stones over the entrance to the cave so that other crocodiles could not come in and disturb him. Then he said to Indra. 'You are my wife now. I'll sleep with you.'

Wilar did not leave the cave for several days. When his belly became empty again he had to come out and look for food. Before he left the cave he blocked the entrance with mud and stones to keep the girl safe from the other crocodiles and to prevent her running away.

When Indra found herself alone she began to break through the entrance but the stones were heavy and it was hard to shift them. She could not do it with her hands so she tied her hair around the stones and with it she began to pull the stones away from the mud.

When she had made a hole in the entrance she tried to pass through it. She went out from the cave with her head and chest

but she had a big belly and she could not squeeze any further through the hole. She had to come back into the cave and make the hole bigger. When it was big enough she pushed her way through and ran away.

The people from Indra's tribe were looking for her everywhere. With them was her sister Jippi. They were in the bush and Jippi was the first one to see Indra running from the cave.

'Look,' Jippi said to the others, 'my sister is coming back.'

When Indra reached them Jippi said again, 'Sister, why is your belly so big? You must have eaten many fish.'

Indra did not answer her. She squatted down close to the ground and from her belly there came out one by one a big heap of crocodile eggs. The men from the tribe hit the eggs with their clubs. But as soon as they broke the eggs a frog came out from each egg and jumped away. That is how the frogs first came. Some of them went to the water and some went to the bush. They can live in both places because the both places were the countries of their origin. The frog does not have any hair because Indra lost all her hair pulling out the stones from the entrance to the cave.

KOMPAGNIN and HIS THREE SONS

A long time ago, Kompagnin, the Willy-Willy Man, had a large shell-nut and carried it all the time on a rope round his neck. In it he kept the spirits of his three sons. The boys, Jombol, the Sea Wind; Muruwook, the Inland Wind and Kunubriar, the East Wind were already grown up, but they could not leave their father and go to live on their own.

The boys were kept in the shell-nut most of the time. When Kompagnin needed them to help him hunting or fishing he would rub the shell-nut and they would come out one by one. Then he would give them their spears and the boys would go with him for a while to look for animals, yams or fish.

In the evenings they camped together. Kompagnin played the Didgeridoo and the boys danced. But before he went to sleep he would change his sons into spirits again and put them back into the shell-nut. One day after Big Purra, the Storm, the boys were looking for fish along the sea-shore. Jombol was in the water. He went to the big rocks of the sea to see if there were any crabs.

Kompagnin was on the beach lying in the shade and waiting for his sons to bring him many fish and crabs. But the boys came back without any. Instead they brought back a beautiful girl, Angula, with them.

'I sent you to look for food, not for women,' said Kompagnin. 'Where did you find her?'

'There, lying on the sea rocks,' answered Jombol. 'She is mine. I found her.'

'She is Kagnimin, the Sun's daughter,' Kompagnin told him. 'She has come down from the sky with the Big Purra.'

'She is mine,' said Muruwook, 'I'm the oldest son.'

'She is not yours, but mine,' said Kunubriar. 'I helped Jombol and carried her from the rocks to here.'

Muruwook took his spear in one hand and the girl in the other hand. 'She is my wife,' he said. 'If anyone does not like it, he can fight.'

The two other brothers grabbed their spears and were about to attack Muruwook but Kompagnin stopped them.

'No-one can fight here,' he said. 'I'll do it another way.'

He went to Muruwook and took the girl from his arms. Kompagnin had seen many women before but no one was so beautiful and young as Angula.

'I'm an old man,' he said to himself. 'I should have her for my wife.'

The boys grew impatient and Kunubriar asked, 'Father to whom are you going to give her?'

Kompagnin did not answer. He took the shell-nut. He looked at it for a while and looked at his sons and then he threw the shell-nut into the sea.

'You go and hunt now,' he told the boys. 'Try to find as much food as you can. When you come back in the evening I'll tell you who can have the girl.'

He sent the boys three different ways so that they would not meet and fight. Jombol went to the sea to look for fish, Muruwook went inland to hunt animals and Kunubriar was sent to the East to look for yams.

When he was left alone with the girl, Kompagnin took her with him and walked along the beach. He walked a long way and before the sun set he came to a cave. He knew when the boys came back from the hunt they would follow his tracks and he said to the girl, 'You stay here. I'm going away for a while. I'll be back soon.'

He rose into the air and turned himself into a Willy-Willy and

went back along the shore to blow the sand and cover his tracks. But at that time the rain came and with the rain a large rainbow appeared in the sky. One of its ends rested at the entrance to the cave. Angula came out from the cave and walked over the rainbow back to the sky to live there among the stars.

When Kompagnin came back he saw the empty cave and he said to himself, 'Those boys have tricked me. I'm going to find them and the girl.'

He went to look for the boys but the boys changed themselves into the winds. They went and blew wildly over the country and the sea. And they blew over the bush and amongst the trees and all the while they were fighting with each other, and looking for Kompagnin and the girl.

TANNAR, the FRILL LIZARD
and WONBRI, the BLACK SNAKE

In the Dreamtime Lizard Man, Tannar and Black Snake Man, Wonbri were close neighbours but they did not have much in common and they hardly saw each other. It was like this until Poora, the Big Storm, came.

The part of the country in which Tannar lived was flat with small shrubs and the one in which Wonbri lived was hilly and he lived among the rocks not far from the sea. Tannar could not find any shelter from the storm in his area and he ran to his neighbour. Wonbri was well sheltered in a cave and the entrance to the cave was covered with a big seashell.

When he got there, Tannar called from outside, 'Wonbri, let me in.'

'I don't hear anyone,' said Wonbri.

'I'm your neighbour,' said Tannar. 'There is a big storm outside. I want to come in to your cave.'

'I can't shift the seashell from the entrance,' said Wonbri. 'If you want to get in you have to make a hole through it.'

Tannar had to do so. The shell was hard and it was an arduous job, but the storm kept coming and Tannar had to have shelter. After very hard work he made a hole through the shell, but as soon as he pushed his head through the hole he faced Wonbri with his spear.

'Keep away from my place,' said Wonbri to his neighbour. 'If you don't go back I'll spear you.'

Tannar went back but he could not pull his head from the hole in the shell. He tried to break the shell and free himself but the shell was hard and he could not crush it. 'Now I have to carry this

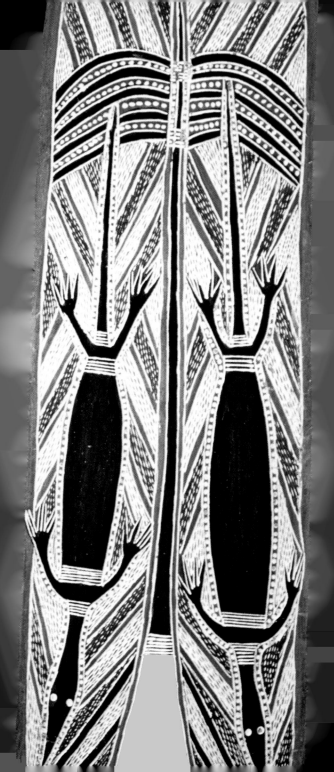

shell on my neck all the time,' he said to himself. 'That Wonbri got me but I am going to trick him too.'

After the storm passed Wonbri went back to the bush and he climbed up on top of a big hollow tree. Tannar followed him. He came up the tree and squeezed himself into the hollow. The shell on his neck would not go in. It was outside, next to the trunk.

Thunder was heard suddenly and Wonbri said to himself, 'I'm going to run back to my cave.' He began to climb down the tree and while climbing down he fell on to the shell and cut all his leg on the sharp edge of it. Then he fell down to the ground and said to himself, 'My neighbour did this; I'll get him.'

But Tannar had already run into the bush and Wonbri could not move fast enough to catch him.

'I can't walk any more,' said Wonbri. 'I have no more legs and I have to crawl on my belly. From now on I'll be the Black Snake.'

Tannar never did get rid of the shell. It stayed on his neck and became part of his body.

'Like this I don't look like a man any more,' he said, 'I'm going to be a lizard.'

Now, as a lizard he keeps his shell tight to his body but, whenever he sees someone he makes it into a big shell. He wants to show he once cut Wonbri's legs with it and he frightens others and makes them leave him alone.

MURROO, the DUGONG

In the Dreamtime when animals and trees were people, the Dugong used to be a beautiful girl. Her name was Murroo and everyone in the country knew her.

On the day when she was married Murroo went into the bush to find some food for her husband. In the bush she found a big coconut. She wanted to break it and turn the shell into a dish from which her husband could eat. But the coconut was tough and when she hit it hard the splinters from the shell went into her eyes. Murroo screamed with pain and rolled on the ground. She rolled like this for a long way until she came to the edge of the sea. By now her eyes were covered with blood from the wound. When she touched the water she thought it would cure her eyes. She would wash the blood from her eyes with the water and she would be able to see again.

'I'll wash my eyes until I can see again,' she said to herself.

But it was the time when the tide was going out. Murroo could not see it. Whenever she wanted to reach the water the sea had moved down a step or two away from her. She followed it and like this she went far away.

Later, when the tide came, Murroo could not find her way back. Now the sea began to rise, the waves rushed on her and Murroo screamed. She tried to fight her way back but instead of making her way towards the beach she went down to the sea. There she changed herself into a Dugong.

Murroo is a Dugong now but once she used to be a beautiful girl. She still keeps some of her human form and she has breasts

and feeds her baby from her breasts as every woman does. Sometimes one can hear her crying far out over the sea. This is the cry of Murroo lost in the water.

VIRRA BIRRON, the WILLY-WILLY
and MINGOR, the ANT

A long time ago Virra Birron flew wildly over the country. He whirlpooled in the air pulling up the trees and raising clouds of dust and nothing could please him or calm him down or make him change his way of travelling. Only when he felt tired of travelling would he come down to the ground and change himself into a man. Then he looked bigger than any tree in the country. No one liked him because he was strong and spoke loudly and frightened everyone and the people kept away from him.

It did not bother Virra Birron that he never had any friends because he did not wish to have friends. While he was down on the ground he wandered around hunting and dancing and he hardly noticed that there was anyone else living in the country.

One day Virra Birron was coming up from the beach carrying a big fish on his shoulders. It was so large that it hung over his shoulders with its tail sweeping the ground. As he walked towards the bush with the fish he met Mingor, the Ant-Man.

'It is a nice catch,' said Mingor.

'Speak loudly; I can't hear you,' thundered Virra Birron with his voice.

'Can I have a bit of fish?' asked Mingor.

'It is mine; go away.'

'I can make a fire for you,' said Mingor. 'I'll bring a lot of wood, all you need to cook it.'

'I'll blow you into the air if you don't go away,' threatened Virra Birron.

But Mingor was hungry and the fish was big. He thought he ought to have a piece of it and he tried once again.

'Please,' he said. 'Let me go with you. After you eat the fish I can have the bones to pick.'

'It is mine,' said Virra Birron. 'I'll throw them away.'

'I'll find the bones in the bush and eat them.'

'I'll throw the bones far away into the sea.'

Mingor did not want to go away without having a piece of the fish. He followed Virra Birron furtively. He did not have to go a long way. As soon as Virra Birron reached the bush he found a spot for his camping place. Then he pulled out some of the trees and made a big fire. By now he was tired and he lay down to sleep without cooking the fish.

While he was asleep Mingor came to him and took the fish away. The fish was too heavy for Mingor to carry. As he went away through the bush he kept cutting off pieces of the fish. He called to everyone around to come to him and have the pieces of the fish.

Virra Birron slept for several days. When he awoke he said, 'I'm going to get Mingor. When I catch him I'll lift him up into the air as high as the sky goes and then I'll drop him down.'

He began to search for him through the bush, pulling up trees and raising the dust. Mingor was scared Virra Birron would find him and he changed himself into an Ant. He hid under the ground and built a big Ant Hill above him. It is so well built that even the heaviest storm will not destroy it.

Virra Birron is still in the air and often he flies through the bush pulling up the trees but he can never knock down an Ant Hill.

NUMUL, the FIRE
and DARVIN, the FISH

A long time ago when many animals were not yet born a kind man called Numul lived in the country. He was the only one who had fire. He carried it away with him in a piece of wood and he kept it alive all the time.

Wherever Numul camped he made a fire. It was easy for him to do so. He put dry grass on his piece of wood and blew on it several times, then the fire would flame up.

Numul travelled from one end of the country to the other. Whenever he met anybody he said, 'Don't you eat Ammonga, the raw food, any more. Here, I'll make a fire for you. You cook your tucker on it and have Ungme, the cooked food.'

One day Darvin, the Fish Man, came to Numul and said, 'You are the only man who can make fire. Come to my country and do it.'

'Where's your country?' asked Numul.

'It is on the sea.'

'No,' Numul said to him. 'This fire is not for you. If this fire goes to the water we will never have it again.'

Darvin went away and thought of a way to trick Numul. He painted his face and body so that no one could recognise him. He knew which way Numul was travelling and he ran to get on his tracks ahead of him. He was painted so that Numul wouldn't recognise him.

Numul travelled without knowing about the trick. When evening came he saw someone camped by the track. A man with a painted face and body was there eating Ammonga and he stopped to talk to him.

'Here,' he said. 'I'll make a fire for you. You will cook your food and have Ungme.'

'It is good that someone came,' said Darvin feeling happy that Numul did not recognise him. 'I have too much food here and I wish someone to eat it with me.'

They cooked the food and ate the lot.

After the meal Numul took his piece of wood and buried it in the ash and then he went to sleep. Darvin stayed awake for a while. When he felt that Numul was asleep he grabbed the wood from the ash and rushed to the sea. As he ran away he was moving so fast that the wind blew on to the piece of wood and it began to burn. He had to go a long way and when he reached the sea the piece of wood had become coal. Darvin rushed with it into the water but when the coal touched the water the water began to boil.

'Something is wrong here,' said Darvin to himself. 'I have to think of some better way to make the fire not to fight with the water. He was still in the shallow water by the beach. He put the coal on the top of his head so that it would not become wet then he walked out towards the depths of the sea. Numul awoke from his sleep and saw the light of his fire disappearing into the darkness.

'That man Darvin has stolen my fire and run away,' he said.

He jumped up and went quickly after him but by now Darvin had gone far into the sea and only the top of his head and the coal on it was out of the water.

'I'll get him,' said Numul to himself and he ran fast to the water. He reached out and grabbed the coal at the last moment just when it was touching the surface of the water. The coal was nearly dead but he held it up in the air and the wind lighted it again.

'We nearly lost fire forever,' said Numul. He took his fire with him and he went walking through the bush. He stopped at many trees and hit the coal against them and made sparks fly high in

the air. The sparks which flew away sank into the branches of the trees and hid themselves there forever. Now when someone wants to make a fire he has only to rub two pieces of wood against each other and the fire will come out from the tree again.

Numul was good fellow.

PURRA, the CLOUD

In the Dreamtime a man named Purra travelled all over the country. He was a lonely man and he looked around to find a girl for his wife. But wherever he came to he was a stranger. The first words he spoke when he met other people was to ask for a girl to be his wife. No one wanted to give their daughter to a stranger and he was always told to go away.

But Purra kept trying. He travelled for so long and went to so many places that after a time he did not remember any more when and from where it was he first began his journey.

One day he was passing by a waterhole and he leant over it to drink.

'Look,' he said suddenly to himself, pointing at his face in the water. 'There, I'm an ugly old man. Now that I am old I'll never find a girl for myself.'

Purra felt angry at all the people who were married and happy and at all the people who had daughters and who would not give one to him. He thought of doing some harm to them all and he said to himself, 'I'm going to live in the sky and I'm going to take all the water from the land with me. Those that live here will then suffer from thirst the same as I have suffered being without a woman.'

He made a big bark bucket and he began to pour in all the water from the country into it. He wanted to take even the last drop of water from the land to the sky with him.

Kubelin, the Thunder Man, was the first to see him. He was a big man with a loud voice and he began to call to all the other people that the water was being taken from them.

'Come here. Purra is taking our water to the sky,' went his voice through the country. His voice was strong and as it passed by the hills and through the gorges it echoed many different ways. Travelling like this Kubelin's call went to everyone living in the country.

The men from many different tribes rushed with their spears to stop Purra. But by now he had all the water from the earth in his bucket and holding it in his hand he flew up into the sky. The men threw many spears after him but Purra flew faster and higher and no one could hit him.

'I'll get him,' said Kunbabin, the Lightning Man. He was known as the best spear fighter in the country. But by now, Purra was already up in the sky and had changed himself into a cloud. Kunbabin jumped into the air and while he was there he hooked his spear on to his Woomera and threw it.

The spear looked like a flash of light as it went right up to the cloud. It could not kill Purra because he was not a human being any more. But the spear hit the bark water bucket and made a big hole in it. All the water drained away from the hole and fell to the earth in a big rain.

Kunbabin changed himself into lightning and stayed to live in the sky. No one can see him any more. Sometimes when you see big clouds you see lightning and that is the spear which Kunbabin is throwing at the clouds to let the water go down to earth.

Kubelin went to live in the sky too and he changed himself to thunder. He is high up and no one can see him but he watches the world all the time. Whenever he sees the cloud's bucket full of water he begins to thunder and he calls to Kunbabin to hit the bucket with his spear.

OWUD, the SCORPION

Rureru, the Crab Man and his wife did not have any children for a long time. Then they had twins—two boys, but it did not make them happy.

'This last born boy is not mine,' said Rureru. 'He is a son of Cut-Cut the Bad Spirit.'

He took the boy to a big water-hole and he threw him in. As soon as Rureru left the water-hole Cut-Cut came and took the boy away with him. He did not have anything to feed the boy with. He waited for night to come then he took the boy to his mother and changed him for the other twin. As soon as he left the boy there he began to cry.

'Hey, you!' called Rureru to his wife. 'Nurse him. Our boy is hungry.'

Before daybreak Cut-Cut came back. He left the boy he had taken and took his one back. From then on he did this every night, for many nights.

Sometimes the boy was very hungry. Cut-Cut wanted him to get as much food as he needed and he decided to make the night longer. He went up to the sky and rolled over the new cover of the dark and night became twice as long.

'This night is too long,' said Rureru once. 'I can't sleep. I'll go to the beach and fish.'

'Don't go away,' his wife said. 'If I'm alone Cut-Cut might come.'

They slept for a while and then the fire died out.

'I should go into the bush and get some wood,' said Rureru.

'Don't you go,' said his wife. 'Cut-Cut might be around.'

One day Cut-Cut went to the sea to look for fish. He stayed away on the sea and forgot the boy.

The child did not have anything to eat. In the bush around were many cacti. He peeled the bark off the cactus and the milk came out. He lived on the cactus milk and as he grew up he changed himself into Owud the Scorpion.

After many days passed Cut-Cut came back one night. He took Owud with him and went to Rureru's camp. The people were asleep there. Cut-Cut left Owud close to his mother. When Owud sensed her breasts in the dark he rushed to them to be nursed. When he touched her, Cut-Cut stood with his foot on Owud's tail and he bit his mother.

The woman screamed and Rureru jumped up. 'The Cut-Cut spirit must be here,' he said. He grabbed a fire-stick from the fire and threw it into the dark.

Owud ran away into the bush. But from then on whenever he sees human beings he rushes to them. As soon as he touches them, Cut-Cut steps on his tail and he bites.

MARRAWUK, and THE TWO SISTERS

A long time ago, before the first blackman was born in the country, there were two sisters. The older one was called Mia and the younger one was called Mirra. They both wandered around looking for bush tucker. It was just after the Big Rain and the grass was as tall and thick as the trees. The sisters walked around but they did not move silently or fast. The animals heard them coming and always ran away from them.

'We will catching nothing like this,' said Mia. 'It is better if you go that way and I go this way. We will walk far away from each other and the animals frightened by me will run away and rush on to you.'

'Don't you dare go away,' said Mirra.

'Why?'

'If you go away alone Marrawuk, the Bad Spirit, will catch you. He'll lift you up in the air and you will never come back to earth again.'

The two sisters walked on. The grass was now even thicker. But a little while later they came to a wide track. It was wide like a clearing and went straight on as far as the eyes could see. Along this wild track the trees were crushed and the grass whipped away.

'Sister,' said Mia, 'someone big and wild must have passed here.'

'Shhh, shhh, it must have been Marrawuk. If it was he, then we are now close to the sea.'

The two sisters knew that Marrawuk often slept on the sea water. When he slept on the sea water it took him a long while to

get from there to his home in the sky. It took him a long while to get high up in the air. But when he was sleeping on the land and then goes to his home in the sky he makes a lot of roaring noises and crushes the trees and whips the grass under him. When he rises up in the air he only leaves the wind behind him. As he goes higher and higher into the air the wind changes into a breeze.

The clearing led to the sea. When the sisters came to the beach they looked around but they did not see any footprints on the sand. They were sure that no one moved around on the beach.

'We can camp here,' said Mirra. 'This is a good place. No one is around here and Marrawuk has gone to the sky.'

'What if he comes back?' asked the younger sister.

'No. He won't come back. Where he passes once he never comes back by same track again.'

Mirra took a fire stick and started to make a fire. Mia went along the beach to look for food. It was just after sunset and on the sand were many Ruberri, the small crabs that live in a shell. Mia picked up a lot of Ruberri and took them back to the camp.

When the sisters were about to eat the dark had fallen and it was so dense they could not see anything around them. They had to keep the fire blazing to see the food they were going to eat.

Suddenly the wind started to blow. It came right from the sea and began to throw sand on the fire. The sisters placed some more wood on the fire to keep it ablaze but the sand kept coming and coming. It covered all the coals and the last flame died away.

'I know it is you, Marrawuk,' called Mirra looking into the night over the sea. 'Here, we'll give you lots of tucker; eat it all.' She threw lots of Ruberri to the sea but the wind kept on blowing and roaring just the same. 'Here,' Mirra called again, 'have all the Ruberri,' and she threw lots of crabs to the sea.

But this did not please Marrawuk. The wind still kept blowing and was now even stronger than before. With the wind the water

kept coming from the sea on to the beach. The sisters began to run, but the water was much quicker and splashed over their bodies.

'It is no use running,' said Mirra. 'We can't get away. Marrawuk has seen us and he wants to have us.'

'Is he going to take us to the sky?' asked Mia.

'No, he just wants to sleep with us.'

Then the younger sister, Mirra, said, 'I'll go and see him. When I satisfy him I'll come back. He will then leave us alone and we can go.'

The younger sister went along the beach. As soon as she disappeared into the dark the wind stopped blowing and roaring.

The older sister went onto the beach and made a fire. She moved around and caught some Ruberri for dinner. She was not afraid of Marrawuk any more because now he was busy with Mia. In the dark she heard her sister crying. She knew Mia would suffer a lot because Marrawuk was a strong and rough man.

When Mia came back later she was hardly walking. 'I wish I had never gone to see him,' she said.

'He'll leave us alone now,' said the older sister. 'Here, have some Ruberri. I caught them for us.'

But Marrawuk did not leave the sisters alone. Later he began to roar again and he splashed all the beach with the water from the sea.

'He calls for us again,' said Mirra.

'You go this time; it is your turn, sister.'

'No, it is better if you go again. You are used to him now.'

'He is a rough and ugly man,' said Mia. 'I never want to go back to him again.'

The two sisters began to run from the beach towards the bush. Marrawuk threw the water from the sea after them, but the water ran back. So he sent waves of sand after them and the waves from the sea went after the waves of sand. The sand caught the

sisters and it kept coming on and on and it covered them and buried them on the beach.

On the spot near the beach where the sisters are buried two palm trees came up. On one of them nut fruit grows high in the air. The other one was smaller and had green leaves but no fruit. The white man calls them The High Nut Palm and the Small Bush Palm. But they are really Mia and Mirra.

CUT-CUT, the WICKED SPIRIT
and MARAWUK, the SEASHORE PINE

A woman called Marawuk travelled through the country looking for food. She carried her baby with her. The child was hungry and kept crying. From time to time Marawuk gave the baby her breasts. But she was too lean and thin and she could not have any milk. When the child found out that there was no food for her she began to cry again. When the day was over Marawuk did not go back to the camp. She stayed in the bush and went on to the shore of the sea to spend the night there. The big tide was in and Marawuk was hoping that when the water began to go down there would be lots of crabs on the beach.

She tried to make a fire on the beach. But the rain began and all the wood became wet. She rubbed two pieces of wood against each other for a long time but the smoke never came.

'We have to camp without a fire,' she said.

The child cried all through the night. Her voice awoke Cut-Cut the Wicked Spirit.

'Someone is around here,' he said. He rose up from the water and rode on a big wave to the beach.

'Who is here to wake me up?' he yelled.

'My child is hungry,' said Marawuk. 'I am here to look for crabs but I can't make a fire.'

Cut-Cut felt happy that he had met a woman. If it had been day time he would have grabbed her and taken her with him to the sea, but at night he could not see what she looked like and he said, 'I'll make a fire for you.'

He began to rub two logs of wood against each other. It is hard to make a fire in the rain but Cut-Cut rubbed the pieces of wood

so hard together that they crushed and split under his hands. Then the fire started.

In the light of the fire Cut-Cut saw Marawuk. He did not like her because she was bony and ugly and he said, 'If your baby keeps crying you will not catch any crabs. They will hear the noise and go away.'

'She has to cry; she is hungry,' said Marawuk.

'I have a nice home down in the sea-cave,' he told her. 'I'll take the baby and feed her.'

'Don't you take my child away!' yelled Marawuk.

But Cut-Cut had already taken the child in his arms and as he went with it to the sea he said, 'I'll come back with the baby to-morrow.'

The next day he did not come back as he had promised. But a day after he rose up from the water and rode to the beach. Marawuk rushed to meet him then she saw that he was not bringing her child with him and she cried, 'Where is my child? Where is she?'

'I'll bring her back one of these days,' Cut-Cut told her, 'but first—you see all those bushes and high grass near the sea. They trouble me when I rush up from the waves to the beach. You'll have to clean the shore of all the bushes and grass. When you do this I'll bring your baby back.'

Marawuk went and began to pull out all the grass and the bushes which grew near the sea. She cleaned the beach so that only the sand and the stones were left there. But Cut-Cut never came back again. Marawuk stayed on the beach looking over the sea for many days. She watched the sea so closely that she could not even take her eyes from it and go to look for food for herself. She became more bony and thin and at last she died on the shore. On the place where she had stood there grew the first sea-shore Pine. It is the closest tree to the sea and always grows big and lonely on the beach. It is Marawuk looking out to sea for Cut-Cut to bring her child back.

VAMAR, the FLY
and KUGGUN, the BEE

In the Dreamtime there was no sugar bag, the honey stored by the bees. Instead of it there was the Manjil, the sweet flower. The Manjil grew in the billabong, big and red. One day a Bee Girl called Kuggun was wandering through the bush and she came to the billabong to drink water.

'Look', she said to herself, 'the Manjil is here.' She stepped into the water to pick the flower and sucked the honey it held from it.

But the billabong was the Warragun, the sacred place of Vamar, the Fly-Man. He saw the girl stepping into the water and he called out. 'Hey, you! What are you doing at this place?'

'I was going to pick the flower and suck it,' said Kuggun.

Vamar had never tasted Manjil and he did not know that the flower was sweet.

'How can one eat Manjil,' he said. 'You are lying to me. You were going to swim in my billabong. This billabong is my Warragun.'

Kuggun became frightened. To step into someone else's sacred place is a bad thing and those who do might be killed. Kuggun jumped out from the water to run away. But Vamar ran and grabbed her.

'No, you can't go away now,' he said. 'You stepped into my Warragun. I will not kill you because you are a girl. But from now on you are going to be my wife.'

'Let me go back to my country,' cried Kuggun. 'I don't want to live here with you.'

'It is nice here,' he said. 'I'll show you how to eat the kind of

113

food I eat here. Then we'll have children and after that you will like my country and me.'

Vamar went bush and brought back many lizards and snakes. He cooked them and said to Kuggun. 'Here, eat this; it's good tucker.'

'I don't like it,' she told him. She went to the billabong to pick some more sweet flowers. She sucked some and the rest she gave to Vamar: 'Come on, taste it, it is sweet and nice.'

'I don't want to have your tucker,' he yelled. 'You have to eat my tucker.'

Vamar was angry and went back to the billabong. He pulled the Manjil from the water and threw it on the fire.

Kuggun felt sad and she said, 'When we have children they are only going to like my tucker, not your tucker.'

'Don't you worry; I'll show them what to eat.'

Both of them lived a long time. They had many children. But as soon as Kuggun bore a baby the baby changed itself into a bee and flew away into the bush. There in the bush all of the bees lived together and became a big swarm. They fly from flower to flower taking the sweet from them and making it into a sugar bag for their mother, Kuggun.

RURERU, the CRAB
and PARRAY, the POSSUM

A long time ago Rureru, the Crab, was a black fellow. He had lived so long that no one knew when he was born. But even though he had lived such a long life he had never learned to play the didgeridoo.

In the country Parray, the Possum, also lived. He was well known as a didgeridoo player and when he blew into the pipe it was heard all over the bush.

One day Rureru went to see Parray.

'Let us go and hunt together,' he said. 'Afterwards, when the day is over, we'll camp together and eat the food we have got.'

'What will we do when we do not hunt and eat?' asked Parray.

'We'll sing and dance,' said Rureru. He knew that while he had the company of Parray he would hear his friend playing the didgeridoo as long as he liked. This made him happy and he wanted their friendship to go on forever. Rureru never bothered to learn to blow the didgeridoo, so now it came to him that he could hear the best music one could play whenever he wished to.

After they became friends they stayed by the camp fire late every evening. Parray always played the didgeridoo and Rureru danced. They went on enjoying themselves and often they would not stop until daybreak.

But the day came when Parray was tired. He did not feel like playing any more and he said to his friend, 'Enough of this. From now on I'm going my way and you go your way.'

'Why should not we live together longer?' asked Rureru. 'I did not do anything bad to you; we are still good friends.'

'I want everyone alive to hear me playing the didgeridoo, not

only you,' said Parray. 'You have had too much of it. There are lots of others to hear it too.'

'I don't like you going,' said Rureru. 'I might never again hear the didgeridoo if you go.'

'I must go,' said Parray.

'If you must, then—all right. But let us stay together until evening. When the night comes you will play to me for the last time. I'll dance so hard and long that I'll die of it.'

Parray stayed. He began to play early in the evening and Rureru danced. Rureru danced hard and fast and while he was dancing like this he moved backwards from the camp to the beach. He went back so far that even the sound of the didgeridoo could not reach him any more.

'Blow on, Parray!' he called. 'Blow more. What has happened to you?'

Parray blew the didgeridoo harder and harder but Rureru was already on the beach and the sound did not reach him any more.

'If he does not hear me playing, he'll think I have run away,' said Parray to himself. He threw the didgeridoo on the ground and climbed up the tree. It was a hollow tree and he began to blow on it. The sound was now so strong that even on the beach the crashing of the sea waves could not be heard any more because of the sound of Parray's playing.

Rureru now danced on the sand like mad. He still moved backwards and backwards. He backed into the sea but he did not feel the water because he was thinking too much of the playing. He went further down. A wave rushed on to him and knocked him down. But by now Rureru was too tired to get up and go back to the beach.

'I'll stay here and become the crab,' he said to himself.

He is a crab now and that is why a crab moves backwards because Rureru did it when he danced.

119

PURRA, the MILKY WAY and TIRA, the SERPENT

A long time ago, in the beginning, there were not many people on earth and a man called Purra lived by himself without seeing anyone for years. It was time for him to get married, but there were no women around. He wandered through the bush day in day out. He hoped he would find a woman and the first one he saw he would take for his wife.

One day on his journey Purra was crossing a creek. It's water was red and he said, 'Look, a girl must be around here. She is at the time of the passing of blood and went into the water. That is why the creek is red.'

Purra went up the creek. He followed the line of the water. Like this he went right up to the source of the creek. There where it started was a girl. Her legs and half of her body were in the water but the rest of her was lying on the bank.

'She is Tira's daughter,' Purra said to himself.

He went close to her. The girl did not notice him at first, but as he approached her his shadow fell upon her and she turned to escape into the water.

Purra grabbed the girl and when he had got hold of her he said. 'You are the only woman I have met. You'll be my wife.'

The girl did not understand his language and was afraid of him. Purra drew the lines of a man and a woman lying together on the sand and said, 'That's you and me. We'll be husband and wife. We'll live together and sleep together all the time.'

He took the girl for his wife but he knew that her father, the serpent, would be after him. He had to run away and go to another country. But the serpent went after him and followed his

121

track all the time. Purra did not know how far he had to run to get away. He went running for many days and whenever he camped he felt that the serpent was close enough to reach him and he had to make a big fire. The fire kept the serpent away during the night. When the morning came Purra took a big fire stick with him and as he walked away he knocked it from time to time. The sparks from the fire stick were left behind him on his track and the serpent would not come close to him.

But one day the big rain came. The fire stick Purra was carrying died out. With the big rain the creek rose with the rushing water. It was in Purra's way and he had to cross it.

'Come on,' he said to his wife. 'I'll help you to go across the water.'

His wife did not answer and he looked around. He could not see her and he began to call.

'I'm coming back,' she answered from the water. 'My father, Tira, will not follow you any more.'

But the serpent wanted to get Purra and he did not leave him. Purra had to run all over the country, carrying with him his fire-stick to keep the serpent away. But after the long journey he became tired and he said, 'I have to go to some place where Tira can't get me.'

He left the land and went up to the sky to live there. After that no-one saw him again. But Purra is still afraid of the serpent and he is travelling over the sky. As he goes from one end of the sky to the other he carries with him the burning fire-stick. He is not seen up there but he leaves after him a long, long track of sparks and it is seen right up in the sky.

The white men call it the Milky Way, but it is Purra's Track.

PINGAL, the MOON
and YOGAMADA, the SEVEN SISTERS

In the Dreamtime there was no moon. The sky was also without any of the Seven Sisters and many other stars.

A man called Pingal was the moon and he lived on the earth then. He had seven daughters. His wife, Abobi, left him a long time ago. She changed herself into a star and went to live in the sky.

The daughters were grown up and Pingal was thinking of making love to them. But the girls knew something might happen and they never wanted to come close to him.

One day he and his daughters were in the bush looking for food. They came to a rocky point overlooking the big swamp. Pingal came down the rocks to the edge of the swamp and he caught a duck there, and the duck was Majen.

'Come on, daughters,' he called them to come down. 'Here, I'll give Majen to you. Go and eat it.'

The oldest daughter came down from the rocks and the other sisters followed her. When all of them were down at the swamp, Pingal stretched out his Malpirin, his penis. Malpirin became separated from his body and went travelling like a snake through the grass to the sisters. The girls could not run back because the high rocks were behind them. Malpirin came to the oldest daughter and began to make love to her.

Fingal's wife, Abobi, saw this from the sky. She dropped a big rope down to earth and the rope's name was Heripen. The seven sisters got hold of it and they climbed up to the sky. Pingal went to climb Heripen after them. But his wife cut Heripen with a knife made of a sea shell and he fell to the ground. Then he said,

'I'll be the Moon from now on, and I'll go to live in the sky.'

His daughters became Yogamada, the Seven Sisters. They are seen in the sky and they are always travelling together. It is because they are afraid of their father, Pingal.

ARANBI, the GOANNA and VOLAGAI, the BROLGA

Aranbi, the small Goanna Man and Volagai, the one-legged Brolga Woman were married once and they travelled through the country together. When they camped, Aranbi dug waterholes. It was a big and hard job for him to do but he could not let his wife be without water.

Every hole he dug was small and shallow. It caught some rain water, but when hot weather came, the holes dried up quickly.

'Aranbi, you have to do something about it,' Volagai told her husband. 'There is not much water in the hole. Whenever I go in my legs get stuck in the mud.'

Aranbi did not mind drinking muddy water and it never worried him how deep the water was in the hole. But he could not bear to hear his wife complaining about it.

The only thing Aranbi could do was to make Wulmanangan. When you make Wulmanangan you call for rain. He went into the bush and made a big corroboree. He danced and sang for rain to come. But it was the dry season; the rain was far away and could not come to his country.

'What sort of a husband are you?' Volagai said to him. 'You have to do something about water.'

'I do everything I can,' he says, 'but it is not time for rain to come yet.'

'You have to dig a big hole, a hole as big as all this land we see. When the rain comes it will fill up with water, Aranbi. I want to have a waterhole as big as the sea then there will be enough water for me.' Volagai said.

'Such a big hole could never be dug,' Aranbi told her.

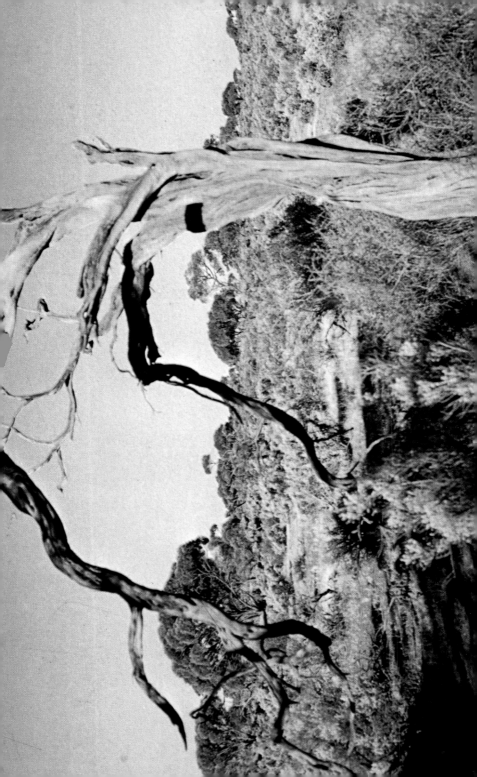

'Aranbi,' said his wife, 'Before you married me, you said you are the best man in the country. You are not as big as the other men are, but you are the strongest of them all. Come on Aranbi, go and dig a hole as big as the sea is.'

Aranbi had no other choice but to begin to dig the hole. It was a formidable job and took him a long time. When he finished it he was an old man.

'You did it,' said Volagai. 'I know you will do everything for me. You are a good man, Aranbi. Now, we'll call this waterhole Wengar, Wengar the swamp. This place is going to be our home and we'll live here forever.'

'You stay here if you like it,' he told her. 'I'm going on my way.'

Aranbi went back to the bush and kept travelling for the rest of his life. He never came back to see his wife or the swamp.

WARUK, the BAD SPIRIT
and PURONGO, the WALLABY

In the Dreamtime there was a big swamp called Wengar in the country near the sea. In its muddy water grew many Garam, the water lily roots. The people from many different tribes came there and made their camps near the Wengar. They did not need to go to hunt or fish because when they felt hungry they went down to the Wengar and dug from the mud as much of the Garam as they could eat.

One day the Waruk man was passing there. He was a pest of a man. He did not like other people having so much food in so easy a way and he said, 'I'll have this Wengar for myself,' and then he shouted to the others. 'This is my Wengar. You can't dig Garam here any more. Go away.'

'You can't do that,' Purongo the Wallaby Man told him. 'This is our country. If you like Garam take some as we all do.'

'Go away,' yelled Waruk. 'If I see anyone taking Garam from here I'll bury him in the mud. He will never come out from it again.'

The people went away but during the night they came back and they dug as many Garam as they could eat. In the morning Waruk saw their footprints in the mud and he shouted, 'You'll have no more Garam.'

He dug out all the Garam from the swamp and carried it to his camp. Waruk was a big man, wild and large like the hill, and he needed to eat a lot. But now when he had all the food from the country he did not go away to hunt any more. He dug a big hole and filled it with Garam. He lay over this big hole near his camp fire day and night. Whenever he was hungry he would slip his

hand under him into the hole and take out some more Garam.

The people watched him from the bush. They watched Waruk lying on the big hole full of Garam. They were hungry but they knew if they went and asked for Garam Waruk would throw rocks and trees at them.

'I'm going to get Garam,' said Purongo.

It was night and Waruk was asleep. Purongo came to his camping place and began to throw sand on his fire. It killed all the flames of the fire, the wood did not burn any more but it made a big smoke. The smoke awoke Waruk.

'Look,' he said, 'my fire is dead. I have to go to bush and get some more wood.'

As soon as Waruk left the camp and went into the dark Purongo jumped into the hole.

'Look, so many Garam,' he said to himself. 'I'll take it all.'

While Waruk was away Purongo cleared the hole. He threw all food from it to the people in the bush. On the bottom of the hole there were only a few Garam left and Purungo kept these for himself. Just when he was getting out of the hole Waruk came back from the bush.

'Purongo, you are stealing my Garam,' yelled Waruk. 'I'll get you.'

Purongo ran into the bush, but Waruk went after him. He could not follow him in the dark night and he thought Purongo might hide somewhere in the bush so Waruk began to roll over. He went through the country like a big hill, rolling himself over the ground and knocking down all the trees.

Purongo could not run away. He knows Waruk is on the way to roll over him and he changes himself into a Wallaby and went into the hollow of a log to hide there. When Waruk passed there he rolled over the log but the log did not crush under him.

From then on Purongo stayed a Wallaby. Waruk is still in the bush and every night he is around looking for revenge.

WARUK, the BAD SPIRIT
and MICHIRIN, the SPIDER

A long time ago there was only one woman who knew how to make dilly bags. Her name was Michirin. She was old and had a young husband to look after her. A few days after she was married to him her husband went bush. He was a good fighter and hunter and he took several spears with him but when the day was over he did not come back to the camp. Michirin waited for him for several days and said to herself, 'He might never come back.'

She did not feel like going into the bush to look for him. She stayed in the camp and every day she made several dilly bags from the Yurru, the long grass. She took these bags and wandered through the country and when she saw other people she gave each one of them a dilly bag.

Many people in the country got their dilly bags from Michirin for nothing. One day Waruk, the Bad Spirit, heard about this and he said to himself, 'I'm going to get Michirin. From now on she'll make dilly bags only for me. Before I sell these dilly bags to the people I first want a big heap of fish and yams from them. Like this I'll have all food from the country for me only.'

Waruk went and found Michirin.

'You are an old woman,' he said to her. 'Your husband has gone forever. I'm taking you with me now. You'll be my wife and I'll take care of you.'

Michirin did not like this. No woman wanted to go and live with Waruk. But she could not turn against him because he was strong and spiteful and could do lots of harm to her.

Waruk went into the bush and brought lots of Yurru for Michirin. He even crushed lots of branches from the trees around

the camp and from them he made a nice shade for Michirin to sit under and make dilly bags all day.

'I'm going to hunt now,' Waruk said. 'When I come back in the evening I want to see this grass made into dilly bags.'

He thought Michirin would do everything he demanded of her. But in the evening when he came back the heap of grass was just the same as it was when he left the camp.

'Look,' he said. 'You did not make a single bag all day. Michirin, I want to have my dilly bags.'

'I can't make them.'

'You are the only woman in the country who knows how to make them.'

'I can't,' she told him. 'If I make dilly bags you will sell them to the people. The people would carry them. Then my husband, who went away, will see the dilly bags and he would know I made them and he would remember me, and he would come to look for me. I don't want him to find me being with another man.'

'That's your trouble,' said Waruk. 'If you don't want to make bags from this grass I'll make rope from it and tie you to the tree.'

Michirin did not want to make the dilly bags. Waruk was angry and wanted to punish her. He made a big rope from the Yurru grass and in the morning before he went to hunt he tied Michirin between two trees. He wanted to leave her hanging in the air until evening and when he came back she would have changed her mind and begin to make dilly bags.

But when Waruk came back from the hunt he could not see Michirin any more. In the space between the two trees where he had left her he saw only a large web instead of the grass ropes. During the day Michirin changed herself into a spider and she was not a human being any more.

139

OCKOK, the OWL
and WAK, the HAWK

Two brothers, Owl Man Ockok and Hawk Man Wak, were from the same mother but from a different father. They did not live together. The country Ockok was in did not have much tucker and he spent days and nights looking for food.

One day Wak came to see him and said, 'Ockok, come to my country; there is plenty of tucker for both of us.'

Ockok went with him. From then on the brothers camped together. Every day, early in the morning, Wak would wake Ockok and say, 'Come on. You go in the bush and look for food. There is plenty of tucker around.'

Ockok would go and spend all day in the bush. One evening when he came back he brought lots of yams with him. 'We are going to cook this now and eat it,' he said to his brother.

'No,' said Wak, 'those yams are my Warrigan, my Totem. We can't eat them.' He took all the yams and threw them away.

'All right,' said Ockok, 'tomorrow I'll go and look for fish, not for yams.'

But next day when he brought fish to the camp Wak said, 'The fish are also my Warrigan. We can't eat them.' He threw the fish away.

Ockok had to go and sleep with an empty belly. But his brother Wak got up during the night and took all the food which he had thrown away. He ate it and then went back to sleep.

One day Ockok found out about this. He did not like to quarrel with his brother and said, 'We are good brothers, but from now on I'm going my way, you go your way.'

Ockok went to the bush and made a new camp for himself.